the BAD GUYS

EPISODE

4

ATTACK OF
THE ZITTENS

A SCHOLASTIC PRESS BOOK
FROM SCHOLASTIC AUSTRALIA

FIRST PUBLISHED BY SCHOLASTIC PRESS,
A DIVISION OF SCHOLASTIC AUSTRALIA PTY LIMITED IN 2016
TEXT AND ILLUSTRATIONS COPYRIGHT © AARON BLABEY, 2016.

PUBLISHED BY SCHOLASTIC SINGAPORE, OPERATING UNDER
GROLIER INTERNATIONAL INC., 81 UBI AVENUE 4, #02-30 UB. ONE,
SINGAPORE 408830. GROLIER INTERNATIONAL INC. IS A SUBSIDIARY
OF SCHOLASTIC INC., NEW YORK, 10012 (USA).

THIS EDITION PUBLISHED UNDER LICENSE FROM SCHOLASTIC AUSTRALIA PTY LIMITED.

ISBN 978-981-11-0685-9

TYPESET IN JANSON, ELO, KERBEROS FANG AND BEHANCE.

PRINTED IN MALAYSIA   FIRST PRINTING, SEPTEMBER 2017
REPRINTED BY SCHOLASTIC MALAYSIA, OPERATING UNDER GROLIER (MALAYSIA) SDN. BHD.,
FEBRUARY 2018

Julia

· AARON BLABEY ·

the BAD GUYS

EPISODE 4

ATTACK OF THE ZITTENS

SCHOLASTIC

(GOOD)

ZOMBIE KITTEN INVASION!

ATTACK OF THE ZITTENS

Good evening.

If there's anyone still out there, please listen carefully . . .

TIFFANY FLUFFIT

Billionaire Mad Scientist
DR RUPERT MARMALADE
has unleashed an army of zombie kittens—commonly known as
ZITTENS ...

MARMALADE: THE FACE OF EVIL

and
NO-ONE IS SAFE!

CRASH!

Even this television station has been **SURROUNDED**. I'm not sure how much longer we'll be on air, but I'll tell you what we know . . .

The Zittens are furry and super-cute but **ABSOLUTELY DEADLY**.

Make no mistake, they will **TRY TO EAT YOU** but here are a few things that may help you escape . . .

TOP TIPS FOR SURVIVING THE KITTEN APOCALYPSE

Firstly, many of them wear **LITTLE BELLS**. IF YOU HEAR A CUTE LITTLE BELL— **RUN AND HIDE!**

Secondly, they **DO NOT LIKE WATER**. Water is your best **DEFENCE**. It really annoys them and can sometimes make them go away.

And finally, they are easily distracted by **BALLS OF YARN**. If you come across a Zitten, tossing them a ball of yarn is your best chance of **ESCAPE**.

However,
if you encounter a
WHOLE LITTER OF ZITTENS,
none of this
will help you.

THIS ISN'T GOOD

If you are set upon by a litter,
there is only one thing you can do—

RUN AS FAST AS YOU CAN!

CRASH!

Oh no! They're inside!

MEEEEOOORGWW!

· CHAPTER 1 ·
NOT GOOD

...GUYS?

Just
remember—
it could be
worse . . .

WORSE?!

OK, that's it.
I say we
throw them
the wolf and
the rest of us
can make a
run for it.

Stop moving around!
You're making the
water splash out of the
paddling pool!

Yeah, cut it out,
Mr Snake!
That water is the only
thing between us and
those tiny flesh-eating
monsters!

Well, *you'd* know
all about **TINY
FLESH-EATING
MONSTERS**,
wouldn't you?

Like you can talk,
**MR-I-EAT-MICE-
AND-ANY-OTHER-
CUTE-LITTLE-
FAMILY-PETS!**

Cut it out, guys!
Don't forget
who we are—
WE'RE THE
GOOD
GUYS CLUB!

Seriously?! *Again* with
that stupid name?

Sorry—I mean . . . we're the
**SORT-OF-INTERNATIONAL-
LEAGUE-OF-HEROES-
TYPE-GUYS** and we'd never
run away from a fight like this,
would we?

We *can't* run away, hermano.
We're surrounded.

And maybe that's a
GOOD thing!

WHAT?!

Well . . . this gives us another chance to be awesome, doesn't it?

OK. I've changed my mind. Let's throw them the wolf.

No, no, listen! **DR MARMALADE**, that rotten little billionaire guinea pig, created this army of Zittens for one reason and one reason only . . .

What reason?

So that we can defeat them and say **'IN YOUR FACE, DR MARMALADE!'**

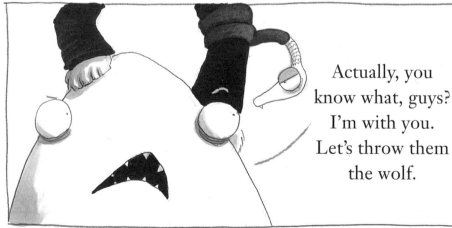

Actually, you know what, guys? I'm with you. Let's throw them the wolf.

No, wait!
I think I hear
something . . .

Don't try to
protect him.
Mr Wolf needs to
'go be a hero' one
last time . . .

Hush up, Slimy.
What do you hear, Legs?

It sounds like . . .

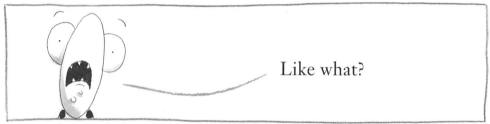

Like what?

. . . like . . .

LIKE WHAT?!

Does it sound like the claws of a zombie kitten *putting a hole in our paddling pool?!*

POP!

No. It sounds more like . . .

It's Agent Fox!

Nice to see you, gentlemen. Climb aboard!

She saved us again!

Yeah. Saved by a girl. *Twice*. This is getting embarrassing.

Embarrassing?!
What's wrong
with you, chico?
We're lucky to
know such a strong,
powerful señorita!

Yes. We. Are . . .

Oh, pleassssse . . .

Oh. One
small thing,
Mr Wolf . . .

Anything!

Would you mind grabbing one of those Zittens for me? That'd be marvellous.

Oh. Ahhhhh . . . sure.

Anything for you, Agent Fox . . .

Um . . . OK.

Here, kitty, kitty, kitty.

Uh-oh.

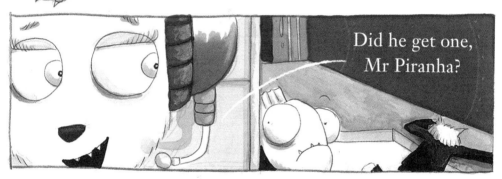

Did he get one, Mr Piranha?

Ah, yes, señorita. I think he's just calming it down with a . . . cuddle.

· CHAPTER 2 ·
TWO PLACES AT ONCE

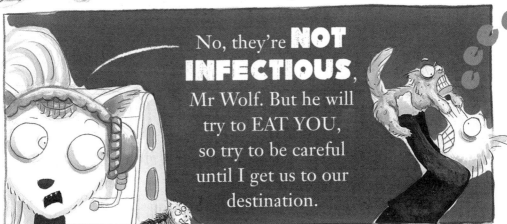

Oh! What a **relief-aaa**aar**rhhhh!**

What destination? Where are we going?

Legs? Can you take the controls?

You got it!

Gentlemen, I know someone who might
be able to help with this Zitten situation.
Her name is

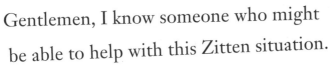

GRANNY GUMBO

and if we can bring her a live Zitten,
there's a chance she can create an

ANTIDOTE

and turn them all
back into
normal kittens.

Unfortunately, it's not that simple.

It never is.

I need to get this Zitten to **GRANNY GUMBO**.

But I *also* need to keep following

DR MARMALADE.

Trouble is—I can't be
in two places at once.
So, Mr Shark?
And Mr Piranha?

Yeah?

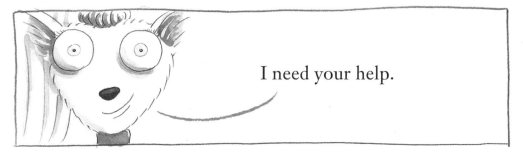

I need your help.

Why us?

Because you two can **SWIM**.

I've managed to track Marmalade to an island

50 miles off the coast of **COSTA RICA**.

I need you to swim out there, in secret,

and keep an eye on him.

And, I hope you don't mind,

but I would recommend

wearing a **DISGUISE**.

Mind? You just made my day. I'm in.

Um . . .

Mr Piranha? You seem troubled. Is everything OK?

Ah, I might have a slight problem, señorita . . .

What?

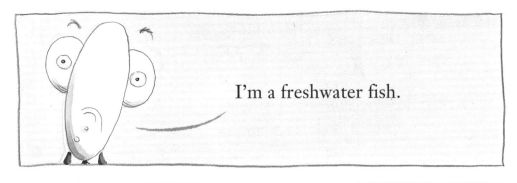

I'm a freshwater fish.

So?

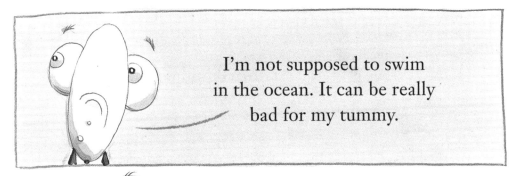

I'm not supposed to swim
in the ocean. It can be really
bad for my tummy.

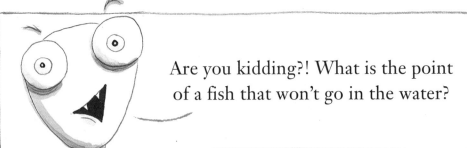

Are you kidding?! What is the point
of a fish that won't go in the water?

So, let me get this straight—you and
Moby Dick over here *WALK AROUND* like
it's the most normal thing in the world,
but you're worried about getting

A LITTLE SALT IN
YOUR GILLS?!

Hmm, I was actually
wondering how you
manage to walk around
so much myself . . .

. . . not that it's any of
my business . . .

Don't worry, Piranha.
I'll get you to that island
safely. And just for the
record—if we want to
walk around . . .

WE WALK AROUND. GOT IT?

Whatever. Just don't get any salt on the Freshwater Princess over here . . .

THAT'S IT!
I'M GONNA EAT THAT UGLY SON OF A CATERPILLAR!

Heeeey! Take it easy, fellas. Agent Fox can hear you. Try to be a little bit cool, will **YOU—**

—ooooohhhhh, my face! It's. Got. My. Face!

Yeah. Sure, Wolf. We'll try to be cool. Just like you.

EEEEEE

Legs? Take us lower.
Mr Shark? This is your stop.
And Mr Piranha?
It's your choice . . .

I'll do it, señorita. You can count on me.
That guinea pig won't get away from us!

Good for you, Piranha.
I'll be thinking of you.
And I sure hope you
don't get a-**SALT**-ed!

Sure. He's an idiot.
But he's *our* idiot.

· CHAPTER 3 ·
GRANNY

I hear you, Agent Fox . . .

Legs? Stay close. I'll contact you when it's time to pick us up.

Stay safe, guys.

Thanks, Legs. But . . . Agent Fox?

This is
GRANNY GUMBO'S WAREHOUSE.

Now, I should warn you— Granny is a *little* bit . . . odd. So you might want to leave the talking to me . . .

Yeah, yeah, whatevs. Hey, look it's open . . . YO! OLD LADY! WHERE'S THE MILK AND COOKIES?

GRAB!

Oh dear . . .

Oh, you sure are gonna taste goo . . .

goo . . . gaah . . . gAAAH . . .

AₐAₐAHHH...

AAAAAA
AHHHHH...

GRAB!

Bless you, Granny.

Who's *that*?
Is that you,
Miss Fox?
I do declare!

But what are you doin' bringing a flea-bitten **MUTT-DOG** into my parlour?! You know I'm allergic to mutt-dogs!

I do apologise, Granny. But I was rather hoping . . .

Oh never you mind, 'cause you brought me a sweet treat, too!

MUNCH!

HEY!
Get this crazy old **ALLIGATOR** off me!

Hush your mouth, grub. Good gracious! You sure are **HARD TO CHEW!**

Seriously?!

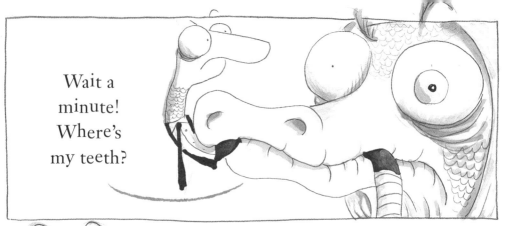

Wait a minute! Where's my teeth?

On my face, Granny.

Give me back my choppers, Mutt-Dog.

I've got my special brew cookin' right now, as a matter of fact . . .

Marvellous, Granny.

Now, I just need a pinch of his **FUR** . . .

SPRINKLE! SPRINKLE!

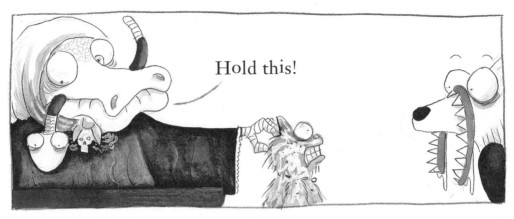

Hold this!

Trouble is . . .

EEEEEEEE

CHOMP!

. . . to finish my antidote, I need a squirt of

SNAKE BITE VENOM!

But where am I going to find me some snake bite venom at this hour . . . ?

Well . . .

Wolf! Don't you dare . . .

Hush your mouth, Grub. What's that you're sayin', Mutt-Dog?

I think you'll find all the
venom you need, right there
in that . . . grub, Granny.

Well, I do declare!
I believe you're
right—this mean-
eyed, low-down,
snake-in-the-grass
will do *nicely* . . .

Now you
listen to me—

HUSH, child.
And hold still.

Wait a minute,
lady. *Have you
been professionally
trained by a vet to
extract venom?!*

• CHAPTER 4 •
the MASTER
OF DISGUISE

OK. Open your eyes . . .

Ahhh . . .
OK. I give up.
Why are you dressed
like a unicorn?

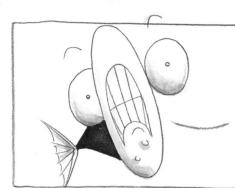

No, no, no, no!
Why are you *naked*, chico?!

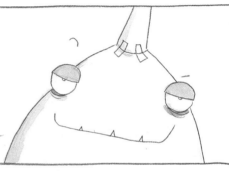

When was the last
time you saw a dolphin
wearing clothes?

Well . . . never.
But you've been spending
too much time with
that bare-butt spider

LEGS,

that's what *I* think . . .

Because THIS little dolphin has a pet goldfish called Mindy.

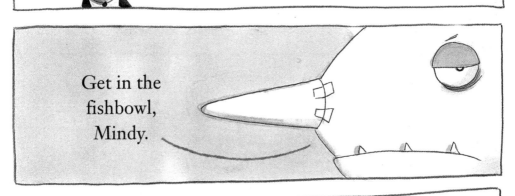

I hope you're not saying what I think you're saying . . .

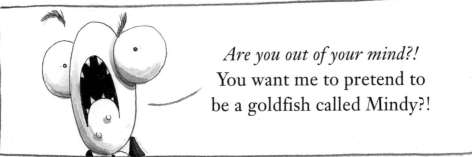

Get in the fishbowl, Mindy.

Are you out of your mind?! You want me to pretend to be a goldfish called Mindy?!

Now you're getting it.
When I'm finished with you, **NO-ONE**
will recognise us. We'll find Marmalade and
YOU won't get a drop of saltwater on you.

I refuse to be naked,
chico! I won't do it!

Calm down **and**
put this on. **We're**
running out **of time.**

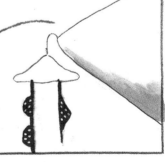

MOMENTS LATER . . .

· CHAPTER 5 ·
the ANTIDOTE

Wha?

What happened?

Hello, Mr Snake. I'm glad to see you're feeling better. It was very kind of you to donate some venom. Granny really appreciates it.

DONATE?! She just **CLOBBERED** me with a frying pan! She's completely *insane*!

Whoa, there! Take it easy, good buddy. I'm sure Agent Fox knows what she's doing . . .

Oh well, if YOU say so, you **LOVE-STRUCK BUFFOON**, then it MUST be true!

Actually, perhaps we could get Granny to clobber him just one more time, *heheheheh* . . .

I must apologise for Granny. Her methods are

HIGHLY UNUSUAL

but I promise you, Mr Snake— she is a genius.

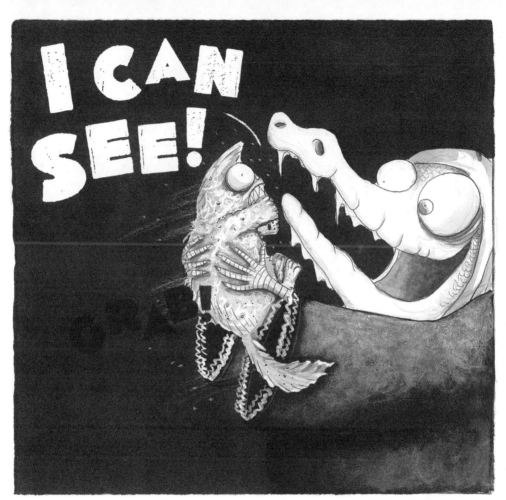

Oh yeah. She's a genius, all right.

I make it from the hair of all the mutt-dogs I **EAT**.

I thought you were allergic to . . . mutt-dogs . . .

Yeah, but they taste so GOOD, I can't help myself.

Oh no! Zittens! We're surrounded!

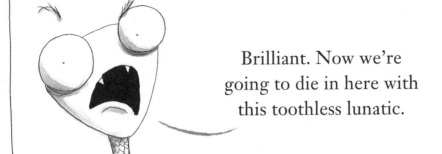

Brilliant. Now we're going to die in here with this toothless lunatic.

Hold it together, gentlemen. Granny? It's time . . .

I hear you! Mutt-Dog, **CATCH!**

Now, watch this . . .

HERE, KITTY!

Oh my stars! It actually works!

You *are* a genius, Granny!

FART!

What did you say?

I'm sorry to poop on your party but if we walk out there, those things will tear us to pieces before we toss even one ball of wool. There's just

TOO MANY OF THEM . . .

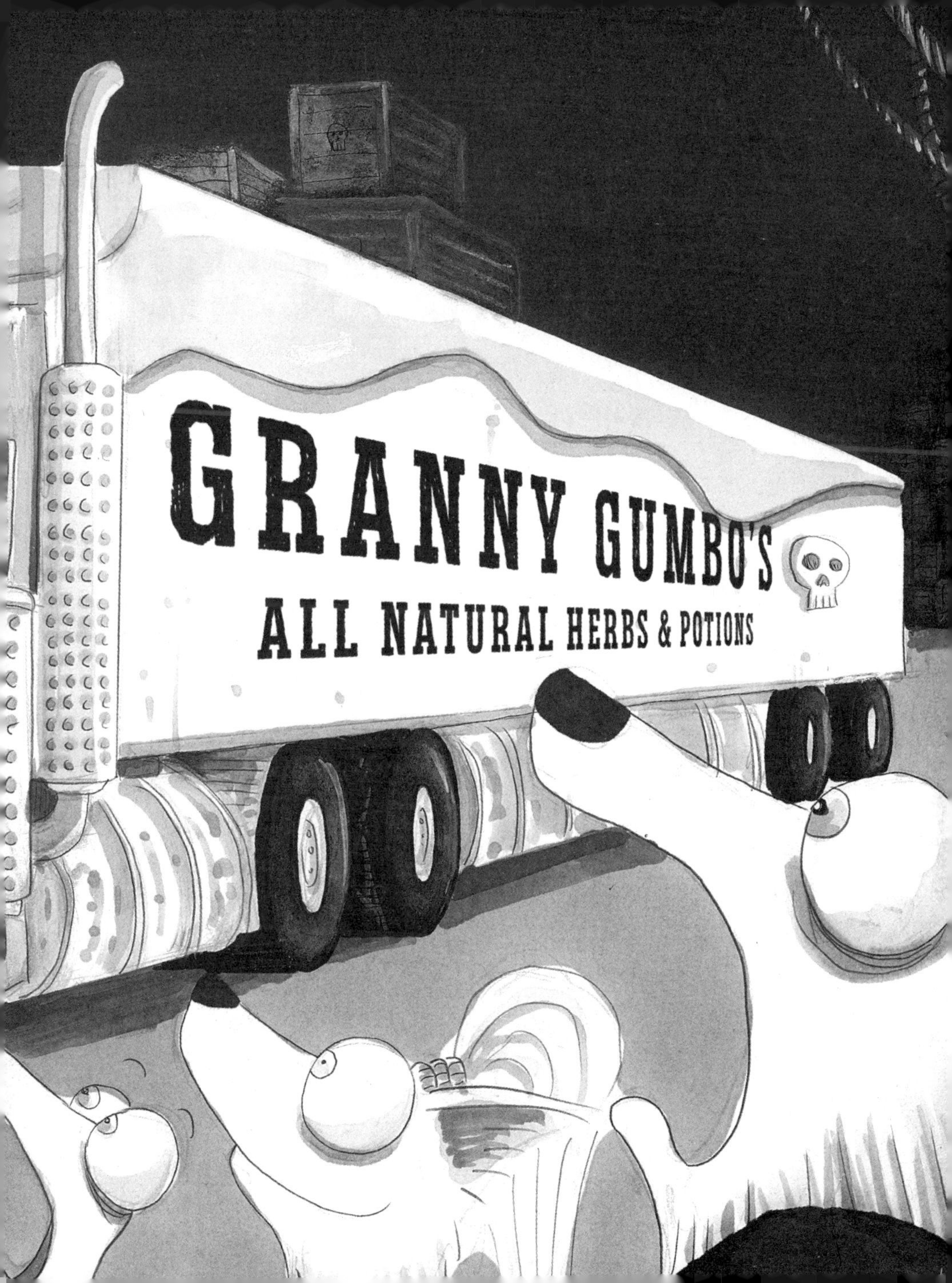
GRANNY GUMBO'S
ALL NATURAL HERBS & POTIONS

· CHAPTER 6 ·
TROUBLE ON GUINEA PIG ISLAND

Here's the island, guys!
Isn't it *awesome*?

Wow. These dolphins
are so cute and friendly!

Yeah.

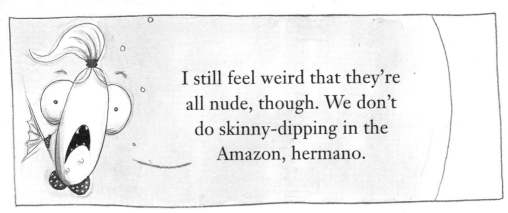

I still feel weird that they're all nude, though. We don't do skinny-dipping in the Amazon, hermano.

I know. It's an ocean thing. You'll get used to it. Can you see anything yet?

No, chico. I'm worried we're too late. It looks totally deserted. Maybe he . . . wait a minute . . .

LOOK!

MARMALADE!

What's he doing up there?
That looks like a . . .

Hey guys!
Let's play a game!

Yeah!
Let's see who
can jump the
highest!

I can't see him. This isn't good.

Man, I thought dolphins were meant to be smart . . .

That's just a myth. Some of them are really stupid.

I love jumping!

Let's jump some more!

So what do we do now? Should we go up there and look for him?

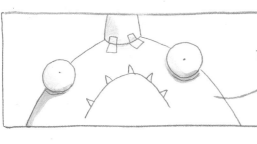

Uh-oh. Somehow I don't think we need to . . .

BOoO OM!

¡Ay, caramba!

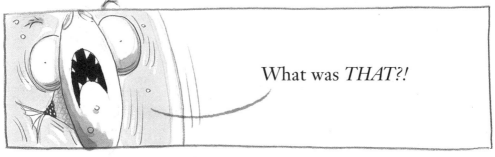

What was *THAT*?!

So where do
you suppose
he's going . . . ?

· CHAPTER 7 ·
KEEP ON TRUCKIN'

RANNY GUMBO'S
LL NATURAL HERBS & POTIONS 💀

OK, gentlemen.
Are we ready to go?

Nearly! I just need to
tighten these pillows . . .

What are you
doing, Wolf?

We're GOOD GUYS,
remember? We don't want
to HURT any kittens.
We want to **SAVE**
all the kittens.

These **CUSHIONS**
and **PILLOWS**
will make sure that none
of them get hurt . . . as we
plough through them at
high speed.

Yeah.

That's the stupidest thing I've ever heard. You've made a perfectly cool truck look ridiculous.

That's just one snake's opinion. I think it looks great.

If by 'great' you mean 'dumb' then yes—it looks 'great'.

Quit your yabberin' and get up here! It's time to hit the road!

Remember, boys—
I'll **DRIVE THE TRUCK**, you **THROW THE YARN**. There are **THOUSANDS** of Zittens so this isn't going to be easy, but if anyone can do it, we can.

You're so awesome!
I mean . . . I just love you . . .
I mean . . . I think you're
the coolest . . . I mean . . .
yeah . . . no . . . yeah.

And the winner of the
most embarrassing speech
award goes to . . .

Don't listen to
him, Mr Wolf.
I think you're
GREAT.

OK, boys.
Let's roll . . .

WOLF AND FOX! SITTING IN A TREE! K! I! S-S! I-N-G!

Shhh!

STUFF!

Wait a minute. That gives me . . .

. . . an IDEA!

YOOOOOM!

That's IT! Whatever you're doing, Mr Wolf, keep it up!

Oh no, you don't! You're not going to use me as a

CATAPULT

again! I forbid it! I—

STUFF!
STUFF!
STUFF!

Nonsense! This is your moment to **SHINE**, little buddy.

The question is—how many balls of yarn does it take to stuff a snake?

Quite a few,
as it turns out.

Oooooh! Look at that
BIG JUICY GRUB!
He's makin' me feel a bit peckish . . .

Hey, Kitties . . .

Hey! *WHERE'S SNAKE?!*

In my **BELLY**, Mutt-Dog, oh yes indeedie!

Wolf! Get me out of here!

You ate Snake?! What is *wrong* with you?

I'm **HUNGRY**, that's what. And I'm fixin' to eat me some **MUTT-DOG**, tooooo . . .

ooo . . .
oooh . . .
ahh . . .
AHHHH . . .

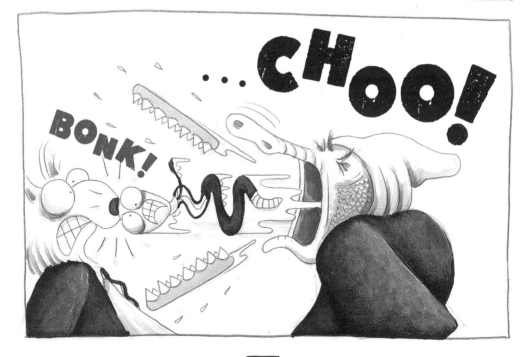

. . . CHOO!

BONK!

Agent Fox . . .

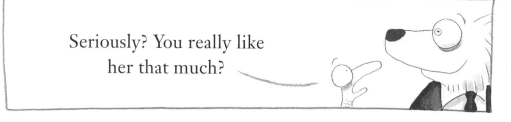

Seriously? You really like her that much?

No, look!

. . . AGENT FOX!

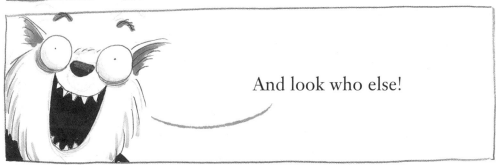

And look who else!

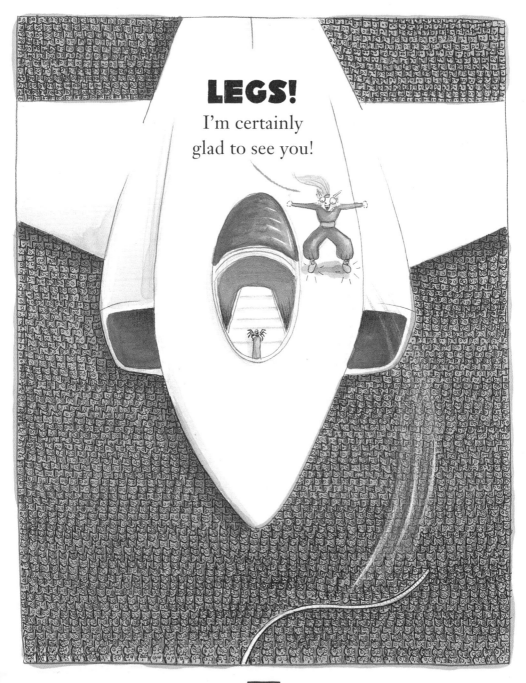

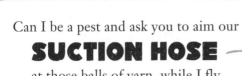

Can I be a pest and ask you to aim our **SUCTION HOSE** at those balls of yarn, while I fly the plane?

Sounds good to me!

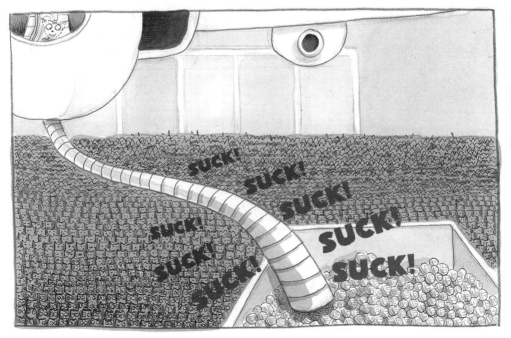

SUCK! SUCK! SUCK! SUCK! SUCK! SUCK! SUCK! SUCK!

OK, that ought to do it.
Now . . . let's put a stop to
this nonsense, shall we?

You didn't *really* think it would be THAT easy, did you?

· CHAPTER 8 ·
the BAD PENNY

Hi, everybody!
Listen carefully because I have a special, private message— just for **YOU!** Aren't you lucky? First of all, congratulations on surviving **PHASE ONE** of my little plan.

11:09
23°

SHOPPING C

Phase One?!
I don't like the sound of this . . .

Sure, a few kittens is one thing.

But imagine if I had a weapon SO powerful that it

could turn **EVERY CUTE AND CUDDLY CREATURE ON THE PLANET** into a **DROOLING WEAPON OF DESTRUCTION!**

Wouldn't that just be **AWESOME?!**

He's lying! He doesn't have a weapon like that! That's impossible . . .

Is it? Well, let me introduce you to the CUTE-ZILLA RAY, Mr Wolf!

CUTE-ZILLA™

Just imagine a world where every puppy . . .

bunny . . .

pony . . .

and dolphin . . .

. . . could be changed,
just by pulling one
little lever . . .

...IN YOUR FACE, LOSERS!

Oh yeah. *That's* how I roll.

And by the way, I'd get away from those kittens if I were you. Because no antidote **ON EARTH** will help you this time . . .

RREEOOWW! RREEOOWW!

Well that's all from me, funsters.
So . . .

SEE YA!

Wouldn't wanna **BE YA!**

And they call
ME crazy!

SHOPPING

· CHAPTER 9 ·
A BIT FURTHER THAN EXPECTED

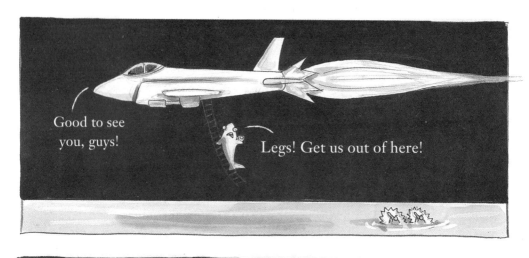

We know, Miss Bolivia.
Nice bikini, by the way.

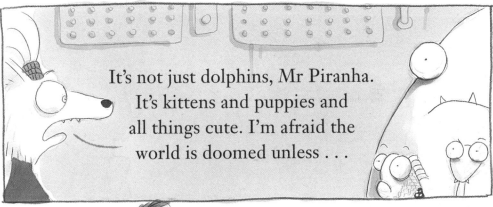

It's not just dolphins, Mr Piranha.
It's kittens and puppies and
all things cute. I'm afraid the
world is doomed unless . . .

. . . UNLESS WE
SAVE IT.

But how?
We don't even know where the
CUTE-ZILLA RAY is.

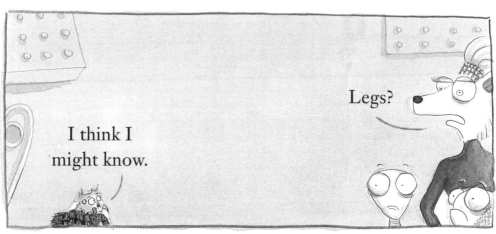

I think I
might know.

Legs?

Well, the only way he'd
be able to use it over the

**WHOLE
PLANET**

is if he's beaming
it in from
SPACE ...

the MOON!

TO BE CONTINUED . . . .